To Sunny
Merry Christmas 2010
Elsneth & Garry

My Country

For my brother John and sister-in-law, Margaret.
For my sister-in-law Val, and in memory of my brother Mal
With all my love – A McL

Omnibus Books
335 Unley Road, Malvern SA 5061
an imprint of Scholastic Australia Pty Ltd (ABN 11 000 614 577)
PO Box 579, Gosford NSW 2250.
www.scholastic.com.au

Part of the Scholastic Group
Sydney • Auckland • New York • Toronto • London • Mexico City • New Delhi •
Hong Kong • Buenos Aires • Puerto Rico

First published in 2010.

National Library of Australia Cataloguing-in-Publication entry

Author: Mackellar, Dorothea, 1885–1968.
Title: My country / Dorothea Mackellar ; illustrator, Andrew McLean.
ISBN 978 1 86291 730 9 (hbk.)
ISBN 978 1 86291 731 6 (pbk.)
Target Audience: For primary school age children.
Other Authors/Contributors: McLean, Andrew, 1946– .
Dewey Number: A821.2

Andrew McLean used watercolour paint for the illustrations in this book.
Scans by Graphic Print Group, Adelaide.
Typeset in Goudy Italic.
Printed in Singapore by Tien Wah Press (Pte) Ltd.

10 9 8 7 6 5 4 3 2 1 *10 11 12 13 14 15 / 0*

My Country

Written by *Dorothea Mackellar*

Illustrated by *Andrew McLean*

An Omnibus Book from Scholastic Australia

The love of field and coppice,
Of green and shaded lanes,
Of ordered woods and gardens
Is running in your veins,

Strong love of grey-blue distance
Brown streams and soft dim skies
I know but cannot share it,
My love is otherwise.

I love a sunburnt country,
A land of sweeping plains,

Of ragged mountain ranges,
Of droughts and flooding rains.

I love her far horizons,
I love her jewel-sea,
Her beauty and her terror –
The wide brown land for me!

A stark white ring-barked forest
All tragic to the moon,

The sapphire-misted mountains,
The hot gold hush of noon.

Green tangle of the brushes,
Where lithe lianas coil,
And orchids deck the tree-tops
And ferns the warm dark soil.

Core of my heart, my country!
Her pitiless blue sky,
When sick at heart, around us,
We see the cattle die –

But then the grey clouds gather,
And we can bless again
The drumming of an army,
The steady, soaking rain.

Core of my heart, my country!
Land of the Rainbow Gold,
For flood and fire and famine,
She pays us back threefold –

Over the thirsty paddocks,
Watch, after many days,
The filmy veil of greenness
That thickens as we gaze.

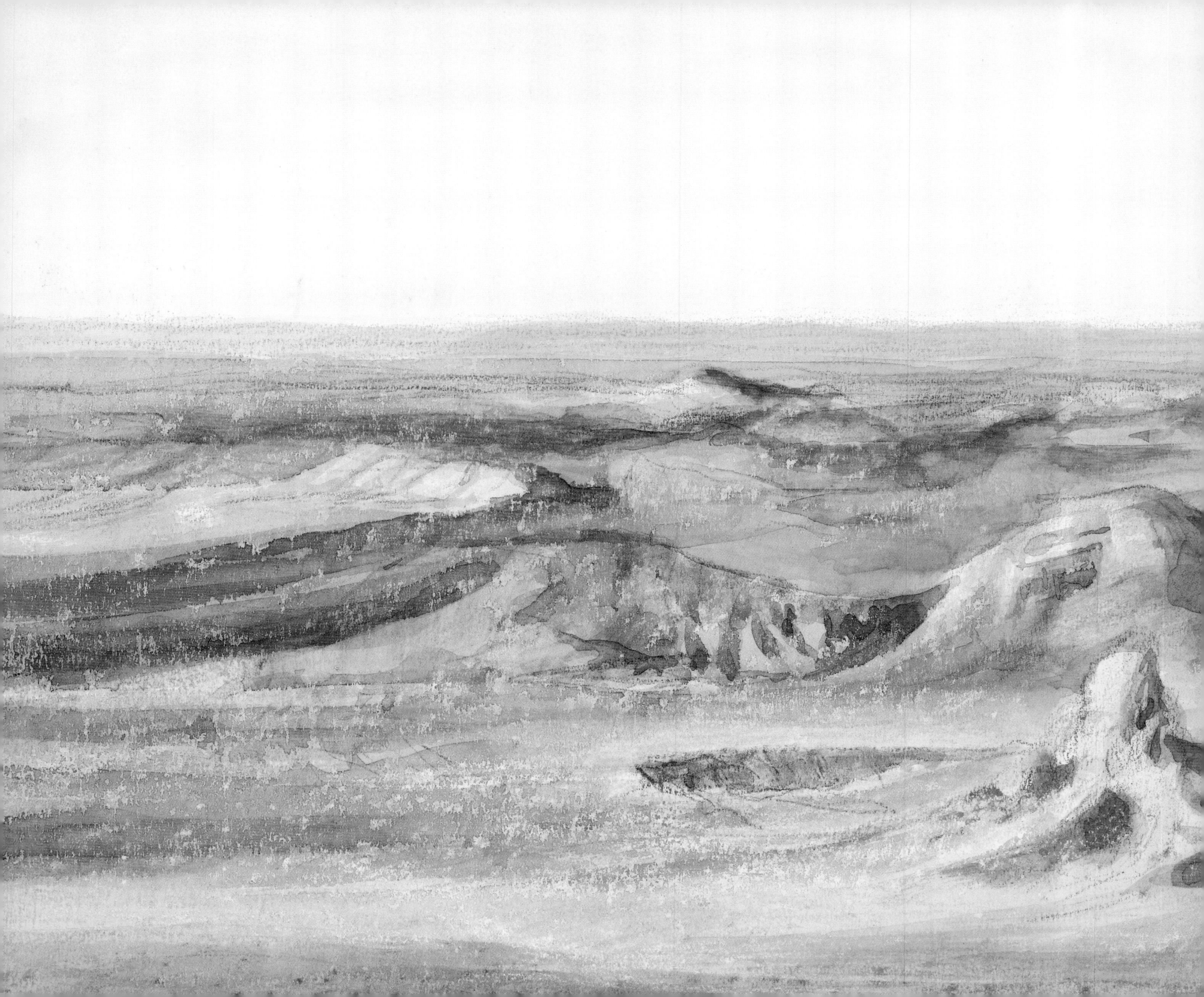

An opal-hearted country,
A wilful, lavish land –
All you who have not loved her,
You will not understand –

Though Earth holds many splendours,
Wherever I may die,
I know to what brown country
My homing thoughts will fly.

Dorothea Mackellar wrote a poem, ‘Core of My Heart’, while she was on a visit to England and feeling homesick for Australia. She was a young woman at the time, and writing pieces that she sent to magazines for publication. Her most famous poem appeared first in the London *Spectator* in September 1908, and was later collected in a book of her poetry called *The Closed Door, and Other Verses*, where it was renamed ‘My Country’. She published three more volumes of verse and also a novel, *Outlaw's Luck*, during the 1920s. She died in 1968.